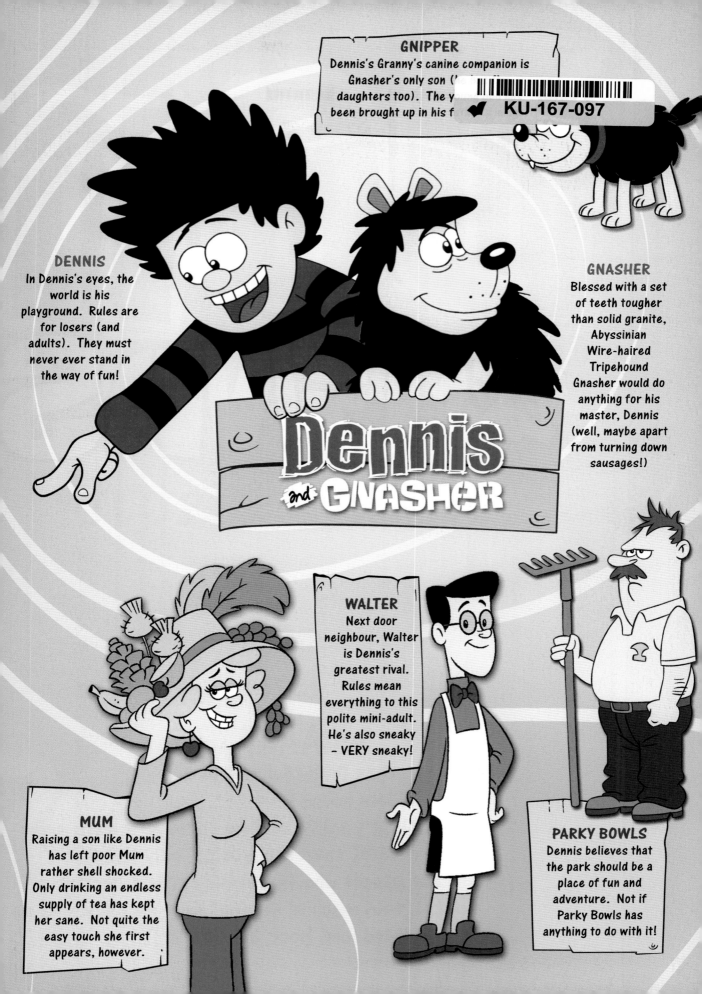

GNIPPER
Dennis's Granny's canine companion is Gnasher's only son ('... daughters too). The y... been brought up in his f...

DENNIS
In Dennis's eyes, the world is his playground. Rules are for losers (and adults). They must never ever stand in the way of fun!

GNASHER
Blessed with a set of teeth tougher than solid granite, Abyssinian Wire-haired Tripehound Gnasher would do anything for his master, Dennis (well, maybe apart from turning down sausages!)

Dennis and GNASHER

WALTER
Next door neighbour, Walter is Dennis's greatest rival. Rules mean everything to this polite mini-adult. He's also sneaky – VERY sneaky!

MUM
Raising a son like Dennis has left poor Mum rather shell shocked. Only drinking an endless supply of tea has kept her sane. Not quite the easy touch she first appears, however.

PARKY BOWLS
Dennis believes that the park should be a place of fun and adventure. Not if Parky Bowls has anything to do with it!

Den and GNAS

and

ANNUAL 2010

WHAAAAT?!?
That frightful ruffian and his
flea-ridden hound have got their very own
annual! It's a disgrace! An outrage! I must
warn readers that this book is only Suitable
for people who find cheeky pranks and
outrageous mischief amusing! Give me a good
hard Sums book any day! HMPH!

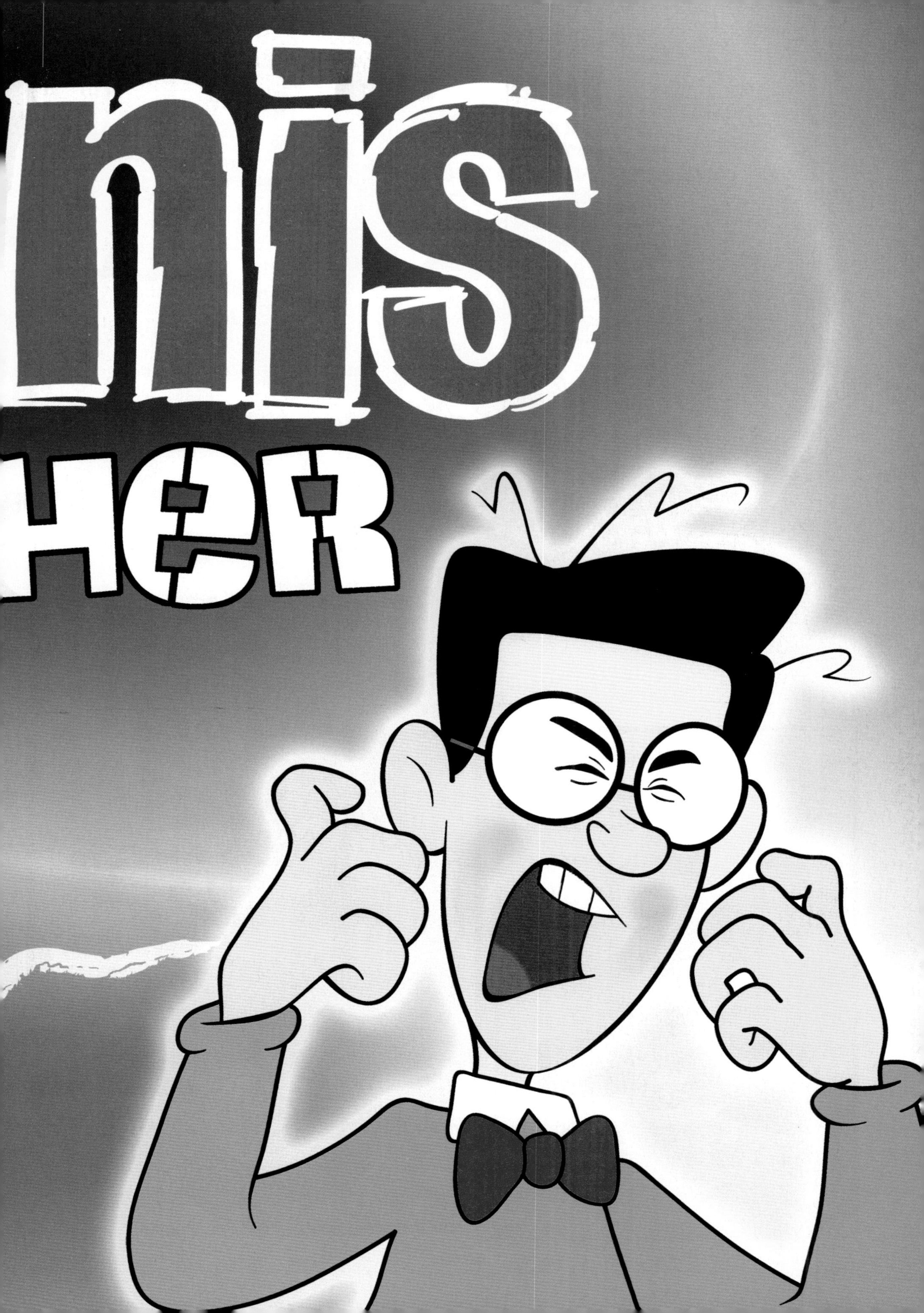
nis
HER

PHOTO-LAFFS

BOO-HOO! ⟵ HEART-BROKEN READER

PHOTO-LAFFS

Something stinks

An Odorous Ode!

Den's sister Bea
was really happy -
She'd dropped a big
one in her nappy.
She let it go without
restraint.
It smelled so bad it
blistered paint.

Poor Mum
stepped in to
change the tot,
But passed out cold
right on the spot!
The Colonel said
"There, there,
my dear!
Best use this
fine old gas
mask here."

As Mum came
round she gruffly said,
"Don't put that foul
thing on my head!
I'll face that nappy -
I don't care.
Just don't mess up
my lovely hair!"

They called a
keeper at the zoo
Who'd faced a putrid
skunk or two.
But even he could
not withstand
The smelliest nappy
in the land.

By then the pong
was so intense
That next door's cat
fell off the fence.
Said Dad "We've got
to change her quick."
At that he was
extremely sick!

The ghastly
guff got so
appalling
Soon folk three
streets away
were falling.
Within the
hour this
vile aroma
Had half the
nation in a
coma.

SURE, IT'S
NOT JUST THE
LEPRECHAUNS
THAT ARE GREEN
AFTER THAT!

ALRIGHT,
ALRIGHT,
WHO'S
POLLUTED THE
MERSEY, LIKE?

THERE'S
NOT A
WELCOME IN
THE HILLSIDES
FOR THAT,
BOYO!

JINGS!
WHIT A
GUFF!!

WHY-AYE
MAN! THAT
WOULD PUT A
BONNIE LASS
OFF HER STOTTY
CAKE!

OO-AR!
SMELLS
WORSE
THAN ROTTEN
MANGLE-
WURZELS!

I SAY!
FRIGHTFUL
WHIFF
WHAT!

At length the Queen began to sniff
"One's nose detects a frightful niff.
Could all my court exhale perchance -
We'll blow that guff across to France."

...An Alien horde from Outer Space Said "Let's destroy the Human Race!" They hurtled Earthwards, evil lot, But what a ghastly shock they got.

Bea's nappy niff engulfed their fleet Their leader, Zarg, cried "PHWAAR! RETREAT! We can't survive this gas attack "Let's head for home - we won't be back!"

If you detect a frightful hum Escaping from some infant's bum. Just think of Bea and don't forget, The World owes her a massive debt!

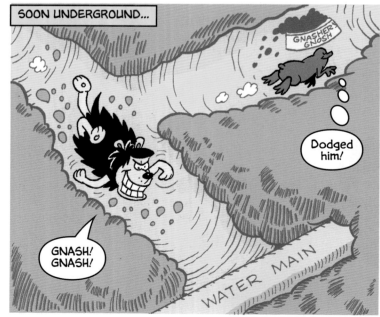

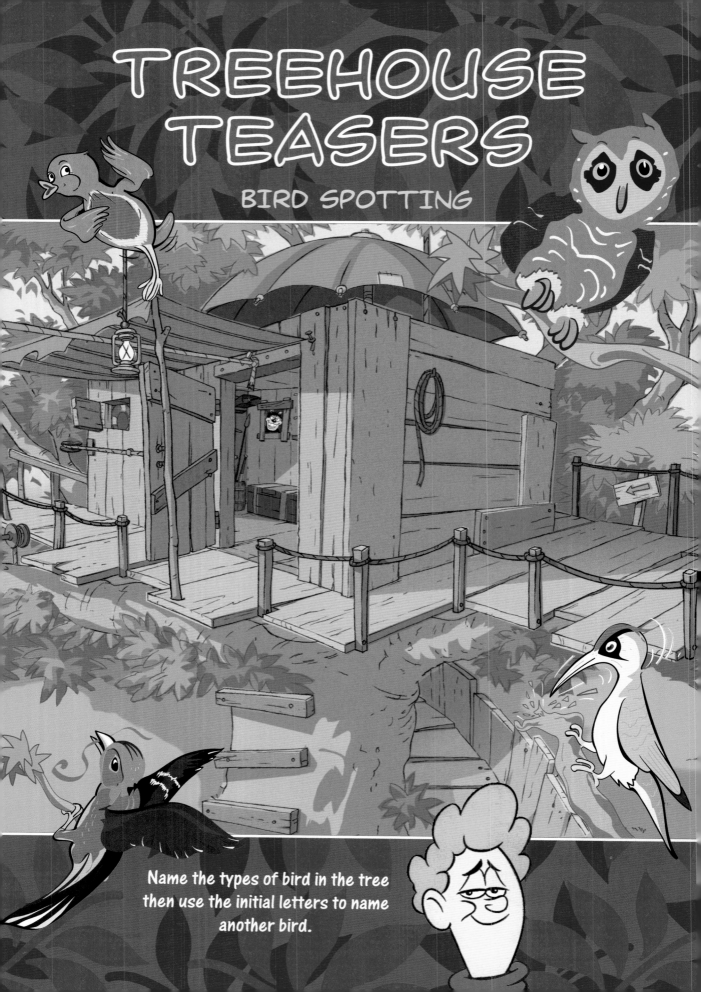

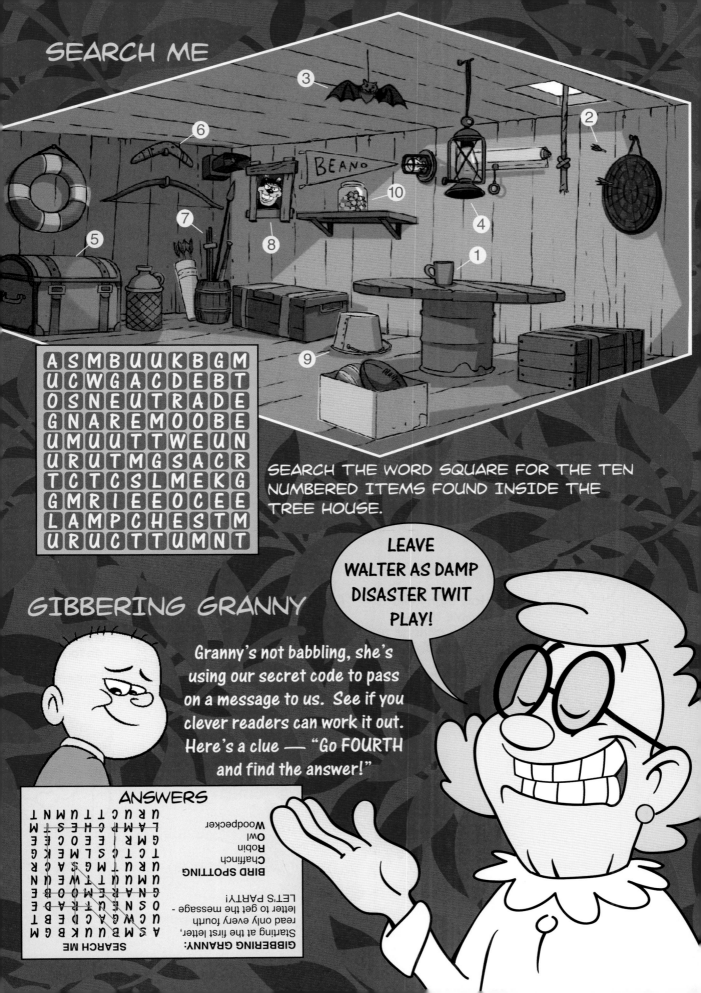

SEARCH ME

A	S	M	B	U	U	K	B	G	M
U	C	W	G	A	C	D	E	B	T
O	S	N	E	U	T	R	A	D	E
G	N	A	R	E	M	O	O	B	E
U	M	U	U	T	T	W	E	U	N
U	R	U	T	M	G	S	A	C	R
T	C	T	C	S	L	M	E	K	G
G	M	R	I	E	E	O	C	E	E
L	A	M	P	C	H	E	S	T	M
U	R	U	C	T	T	U	M	N	T

SEARCH THE WORD SQUARE FOR THE TEN NUMBERED ITEMS FOUND INSIDE THE TREE HOUSE.

LEAVE WALTER AS DAMP DISASTER TWIT PLAY!

GIBBERING GRANNY

Granny's not babbling, she's using our secret code to pass on a message to us. See if you clever readers can work it out. Here's a clue — "Go FOURTH and find the answer!"

ANSWERS

SEARCH ME

A	S	M	B	U	U	K	B	G	M
U	C	W	G	A	C	D	E	B	T
O	S	N	E	U	T	R	A	D	E
G	N	A	R	E	M	O	O	B	E
U	M	U	U	T	T	W	E	U	N
U	R	U	T	M	G	S	A	C	R
T	C	T	C	S	L	M	E	K	G
G	M	R	I	E	E	O	C	E	E
L	A	M	P	C	H	E	S	T	M
U	R	U	C	T	T	U	M	N	T

GIBBERING GRANNY:
Starting at the first letter, read only every fourth letter to get the message - LET'S PARTY!

BIRD SPOTTING
Chaffinch
Robin
Owl
Woodpecker

SPOT THE DIFFERENCE

There are 10 differences between these two pictures. Can you spot 'em all?

PHOTO-LAFFS

Trouble With A 'T'

Crafty Dennis tricks Mr Scrimp by offering a cup of tea, brewed with a disgusting old teabag!

But which string is attached to the teabag?

A B C D

Answer: A

GNASHFLEA FUN

Right, lads. Ready for bath night!

Ha-ha! We're too tough for flea powder!

Yeah! But it's great for making snowmen!

FLEA POWDER

SPRAY!

And for having snowball fights!

Phew! Hard work during the moulting season.

CUT! SLASH!

GASP!

YOU'VE GOTTA BE JOKING

What do you give a constipated budgie?

Chirrup of figs!

I hear you're starring in a play called "Breakfast in Bed". Do you have a big role?

No, just toast and marmalade!

What's green and goes camping?

A boy sprout!

What goes "ABCDEFGHIJKLMNOPQRST UVWXYZ SLURP"?

Dad eating alphabet soup!

What's the definition of bread?

Raw toast!

YOU MIGHT FIND DENNIS AT THE JOKE SHOP...

GNASHER HAS BEEN KNOWN TO LURK AROUND THE BUTCHER'S...

DENNIS TRIES NOT TO BE SEEN AT SCHOOL...

GNASHER IS NEVER FOUND IN THE PAMPERED PETS BOUTIQUE...

HERE'S ONE PLACE YOU'LL DEFINITELY FIND BOTH OF THEM EVERY SINGLE WEEK...

THE BEANO

Menacingly Funny Every week!

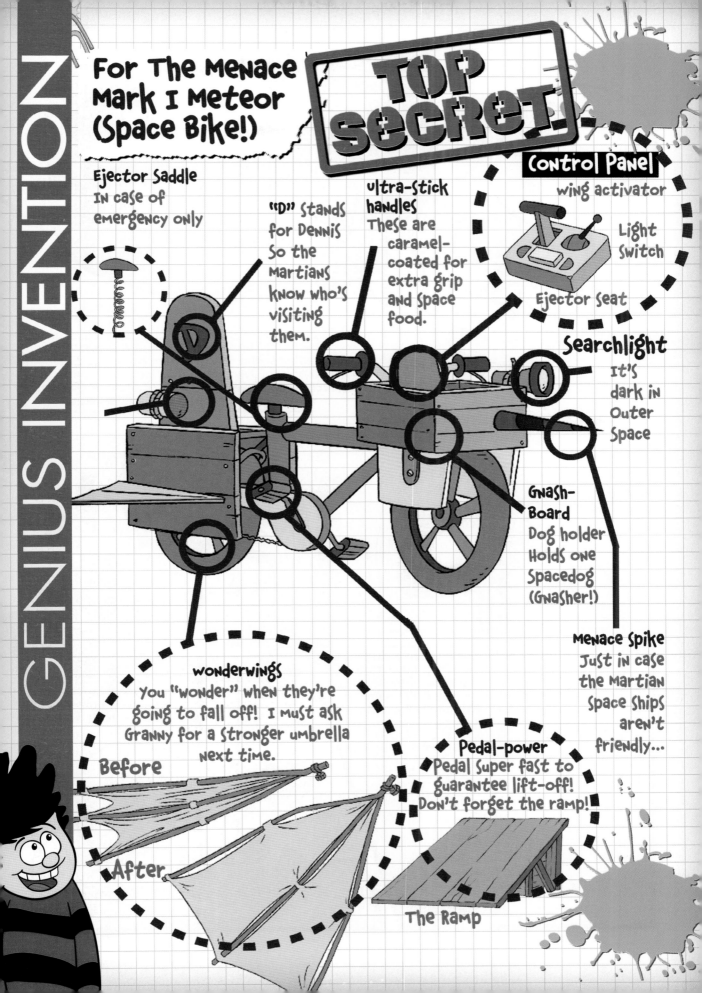

PIE FACE'S WONDERFUL WORLD OF PIES

AMAZE YOUR FRIENDS WITH THESE TASTY PASTRY FACTS!

In Australia they eat PIE FLOATERS - a meat pie floating in a plate of thick pea soup. Legendary Scottish funny man, Billy Connolly is a fan of the delicacy.

BRILLLLLLIANT!

The BIOTIC BAKING BRIGADE are a bunch of protestors who throw cream or custard pies in the faces of famous people including computer tycoon Bill Gates, King Carl Gustav of Sweden and Top Gear host Jeremy Clarkson.

DO THEY MAKE WINDSCREEN WIPERS FOR THE FACE?

STARGAZY PIE is a Cornish dish which includes in its filling several pilchards which have their heads stuck through the crust so they seem to be gazing at the stars - hence the name. It's traditionally served with clotted cream.

I KNOW I'M A BEANO STAR BUT STOP STARING AT ME!

SHOOFLY PIE from Pennsylvania in America, is so called because the sweet molasses in the pie attracts flies which have to be SHOOED away.

SHOOO!

"MINCE PIES" is Cockney rhyming slang for "EYES".

The first pies were made in Ancient Greece hundreds of years ago.

ARE YOUR PIES HUNDREDS OF YEARS OLD AND MADE IN ANCIENT GREASE, TONI?

During Mediaeval times live birds were hidden under pie crusts as a joke to scare people. This is one explanation of the "Four and twenty blackbirds baked in a pie" line in the nursery rhyme "Sing a Song of Sixpence".

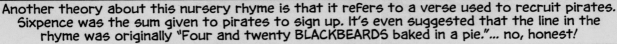

Another theory about this nursery rhyme is that it refers to a verse used to recruit pirates. Sixpence was the sum given to pirates to sign up. It's even suggested that the line in the rhyme was originally "Four and twenty BLACKBEARDS baked in a pie."... no, honest!

OO-AR, ME HEARTIES!

MR HAR-HAR
The Asian owner of the local Joke Shop, Mr Har Har is always delighted to get Dennis to test drive his latest gags. He can also invent some amazing tricks to order.

BEA
Dennis's little sis doubles as a human stink bomb. Her toxic vapours are a potent weapon and can clear a room at the drop of a hat – er – nappy.

THE COLONEL
Lives in Dennis's street and in a world of his own. An ex-military type, he believes small boys should be seen and not heard – not a fan of Dennis, then!

CURLY
Curly is the frizzy-haired right hand man to Dennis (Gnasher's the right hand dog!) If Dennis thinks it's a good idea, Curly's right behind him!

MRS CREECHER
Dennis's Teacher is a Welsh Dragon – a lady not to be messed with! Rules and regulations must be obeyed at all times. Adored by Walter, loathed by Dennis.